THE GREAT BRITISH

CAKE OFF

THE 100% UNOFFICIAL COLOURING BOOK

HarperCollins*Publishers*
1 London Bridge Street
London SE1 9GF

www.harpercollins.co.uk

First published by HarperCollins*Publishers* 2015

1 3 5 7 9 10 8 6 4 2

Illustrations © Harriet Popham 2015

A catalogue record of this book is available from the British Library

ISBN 978-0-00-815953-5

Printed and bound in Spain by Graficas Estella, Spain

FSC

HARRIET POPHAM

THE GREAT BRITISH
CAKE OFF

THE 100% UNOFFICIAL COLOURING BOOK

HarperCollins*Publishers*

Between these pages you'll find over 70 blank illustrations of intricately iced and decadently decorated cakes and bakes, just waiting for you to bring them to life. Colouring brings with it a kind of calmness and fulfilment, a way of being mindfully creative with whatever is in front of you. What I wanted to do with this book was create illustrations where you – the person with the pencils – can feel free to do whatever you want with them. From pink roses and red raspberries, to blue icing, green aprons and glitter hearts – whatever you say, goes. That's one of the best things about colouring; you can be as realistic or as radical as you choose.

I won't pretend to be the star baker in my kitchen, but I love how inventive baking can be, and how inventive it's becoming in homes up and down the country. I wanted to recreate that magic (minus the mishaps and crisped edges) so you can get stuck into the fun bit: decorating. Sprinkling colour onto gingerbread houses, finessing macaron fillings and embellishing sponges wherever you choose. You'll also find at the back of the book some space to add your own drawings, if you so choose, or to experiment with patterns and colours to dress the illustrations with. Who knows – maybe you'll even be inspired to lift one of your creations off the page and into the kitchen!

This is your book to play with as you like; pens, pencils, pastels, paints – these are your cakes for the making.

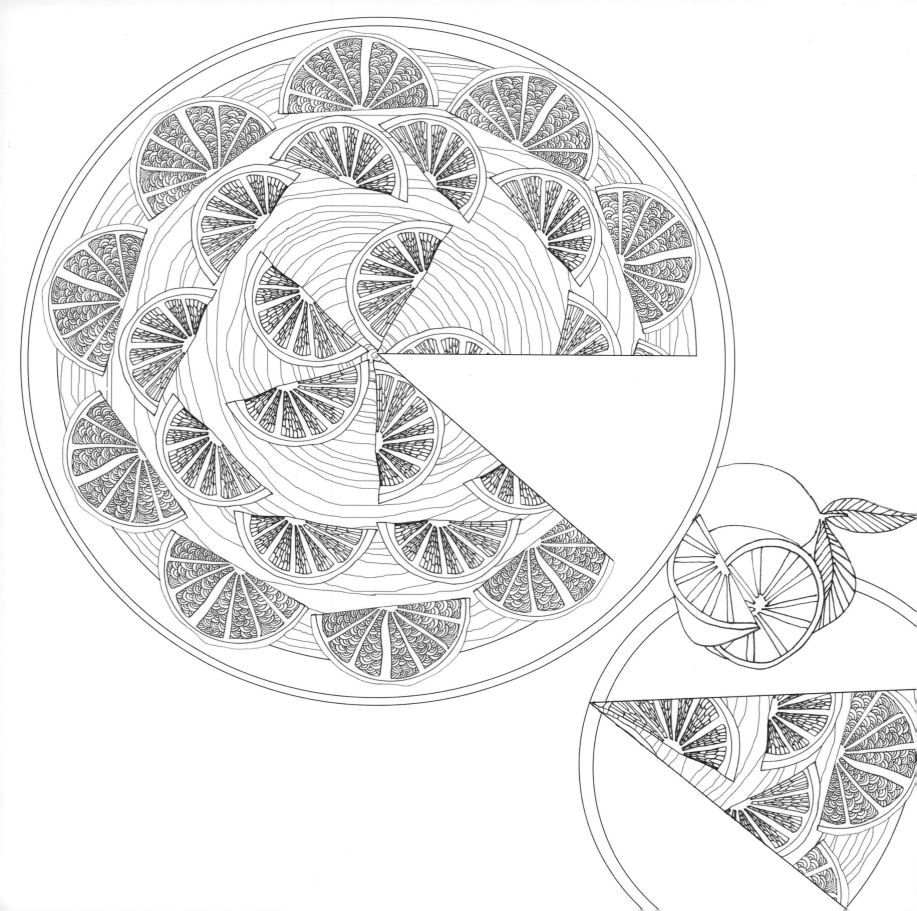

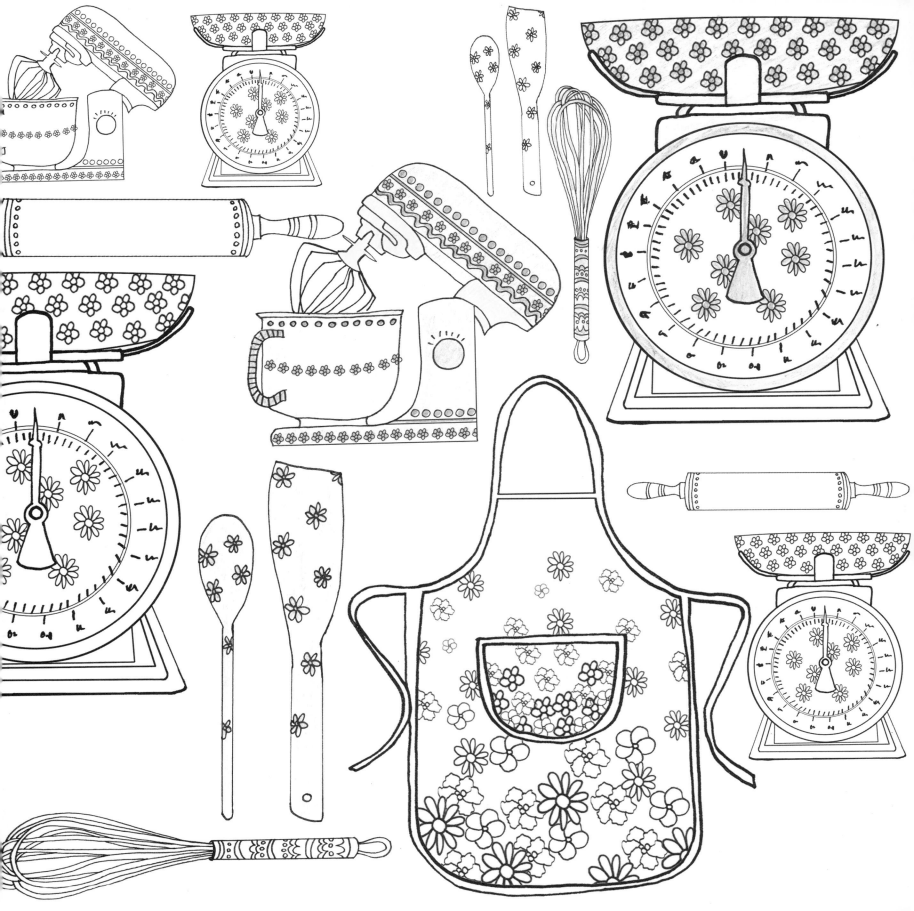

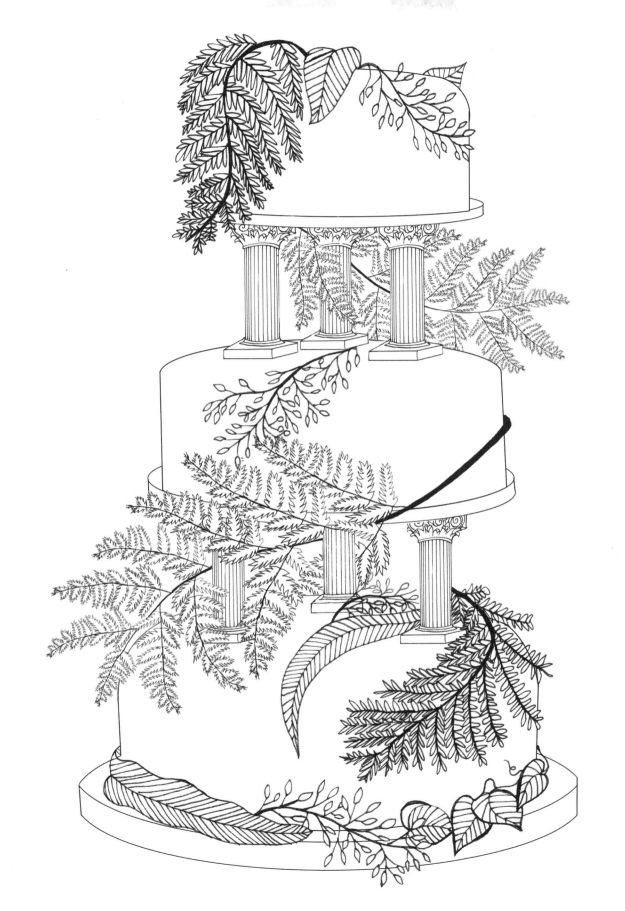

What flavour sponge will you choose for the three layers?

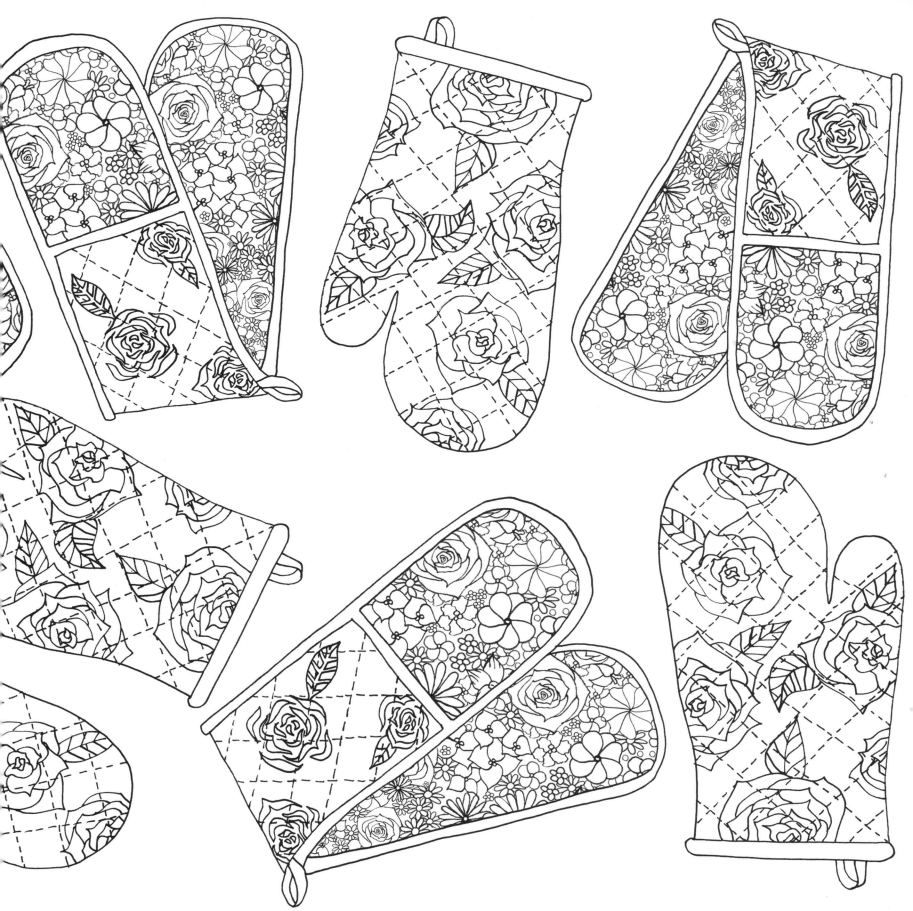

Your own Gingerbread House to deliciously decorate.

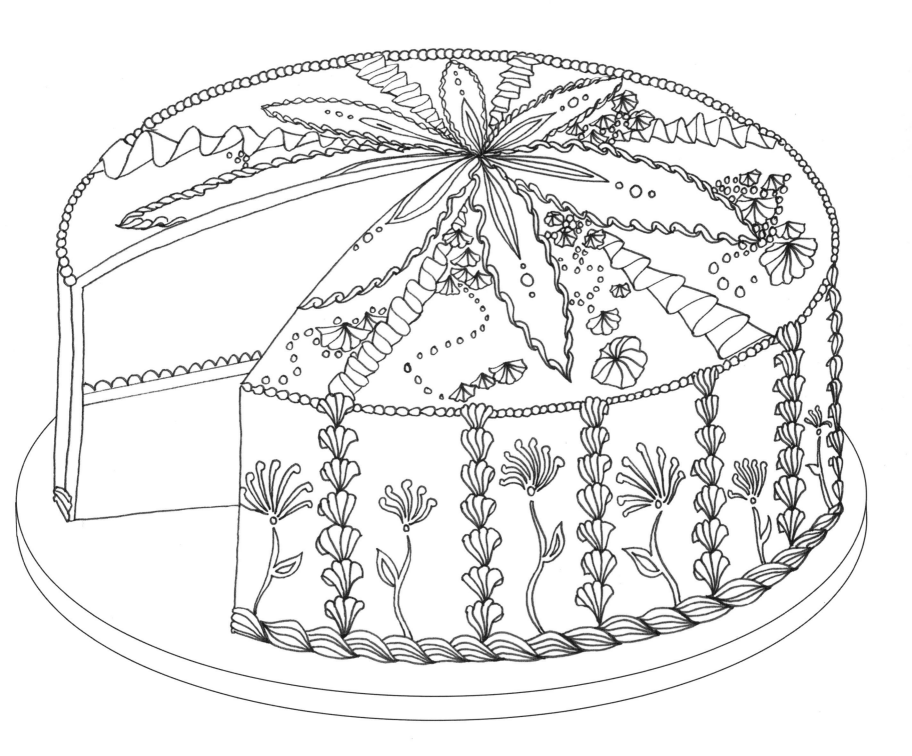

Craft your macarons with every colour you can think of.

A Charlotte Royale is made with slices of Swiss roll and a delicious type of mousse called Bavarois.

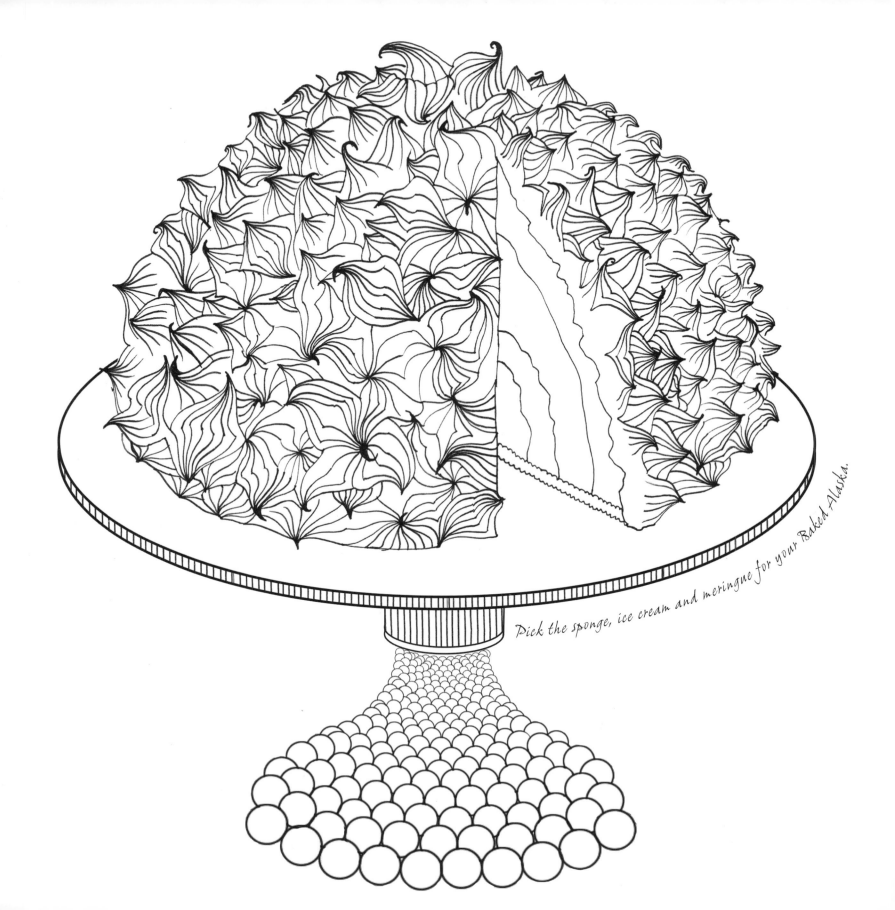

Pick the sponge, ice cream and meringue for your Baked Alaska.

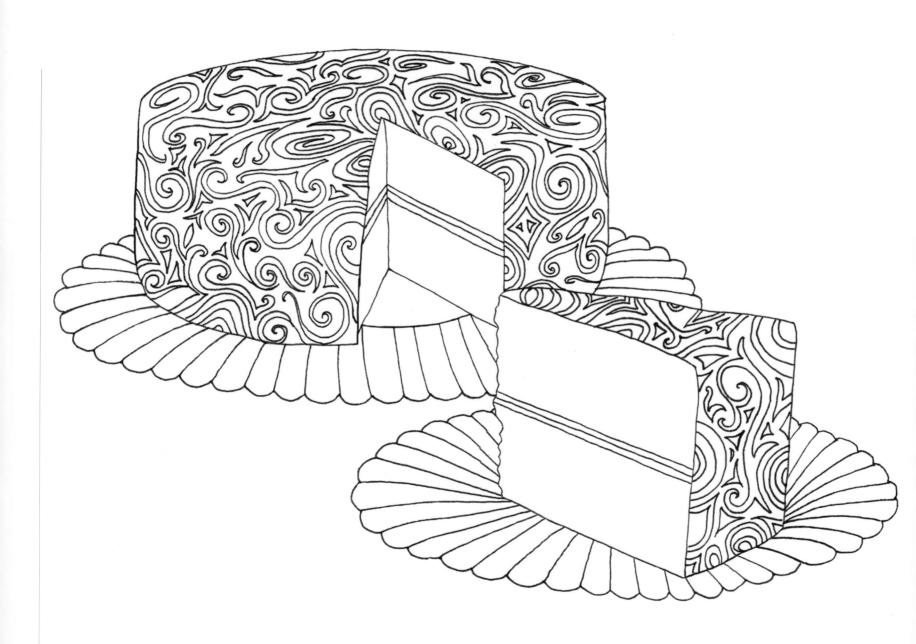

Your Tarte Tatin's crisp pastry and caramelised pears deserve lashings of colour.

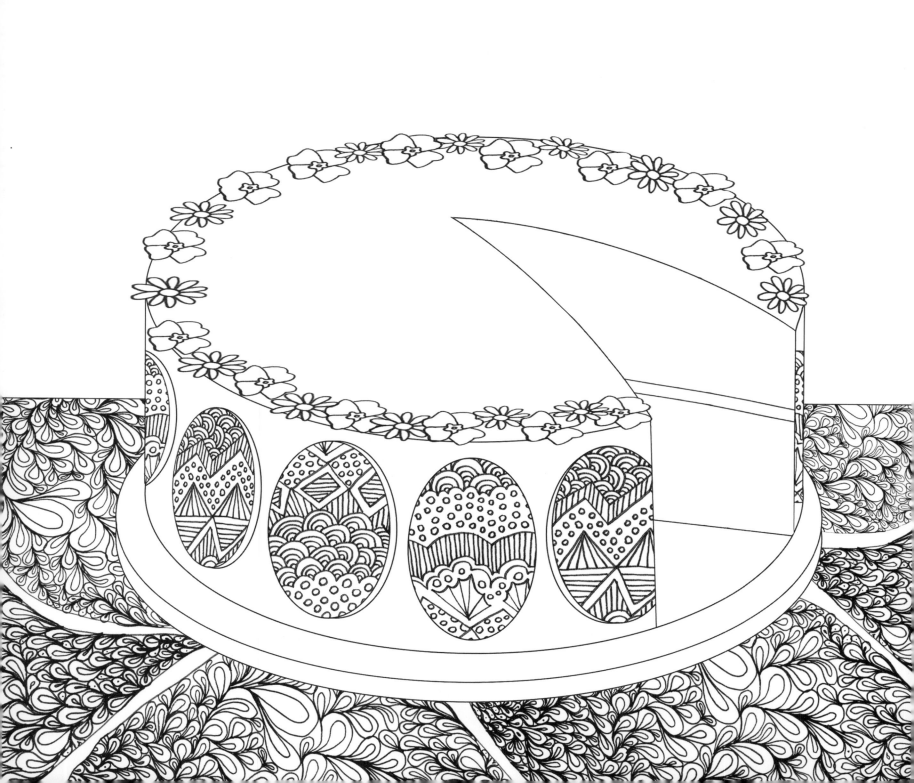

The Scandanavian Kransekake was designed to impress. Intricately ice yours with a range of colours.

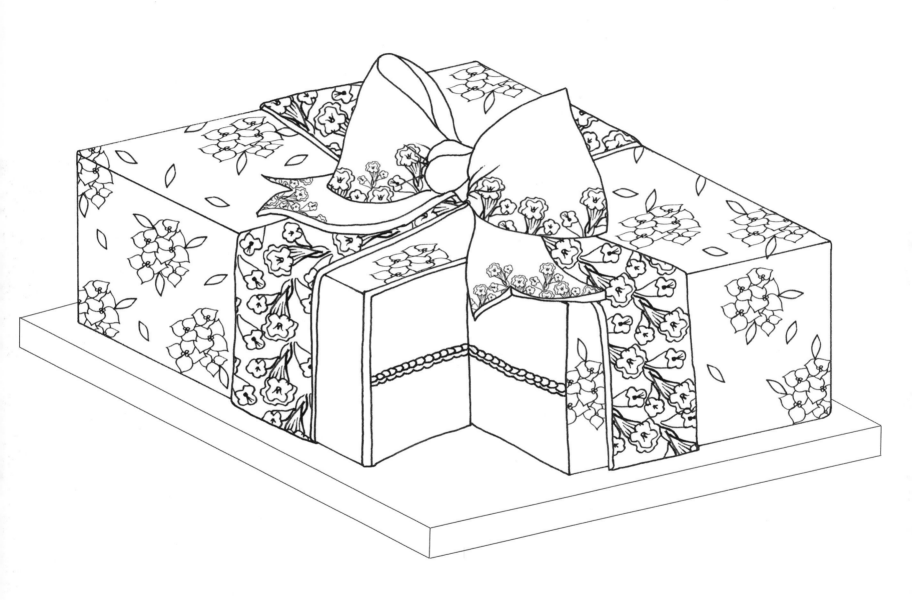

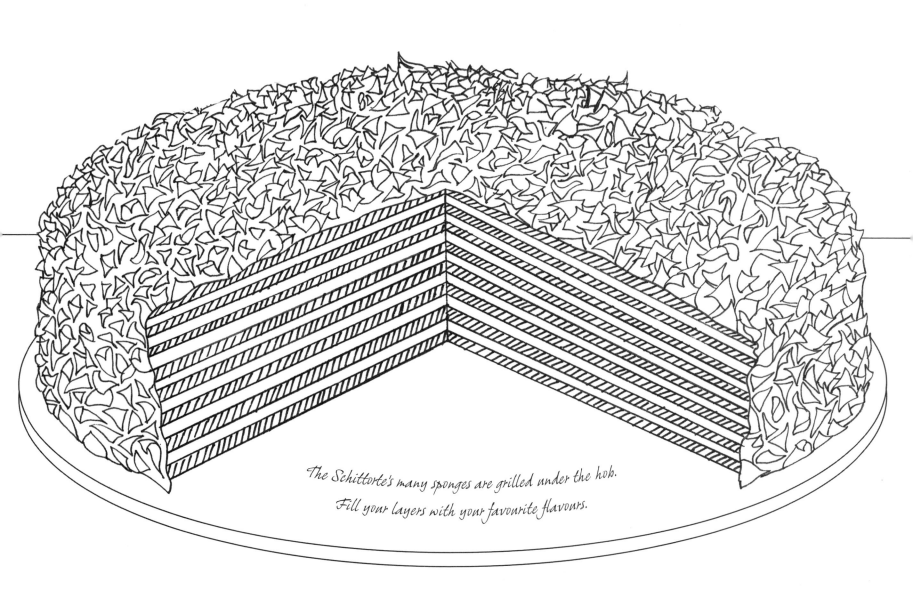

The Schittorte's many sponges are grilled under the hob.

Fill your layers with your favourite flavours.

Pop the cherries of your Upside-down Cake with bursts of colour.

Povitica is a type of Eastern European sweet bread. What flavour filling will your swirls have?

Make your Swedish Princess cake bright green and traditional or create something new and exciting!

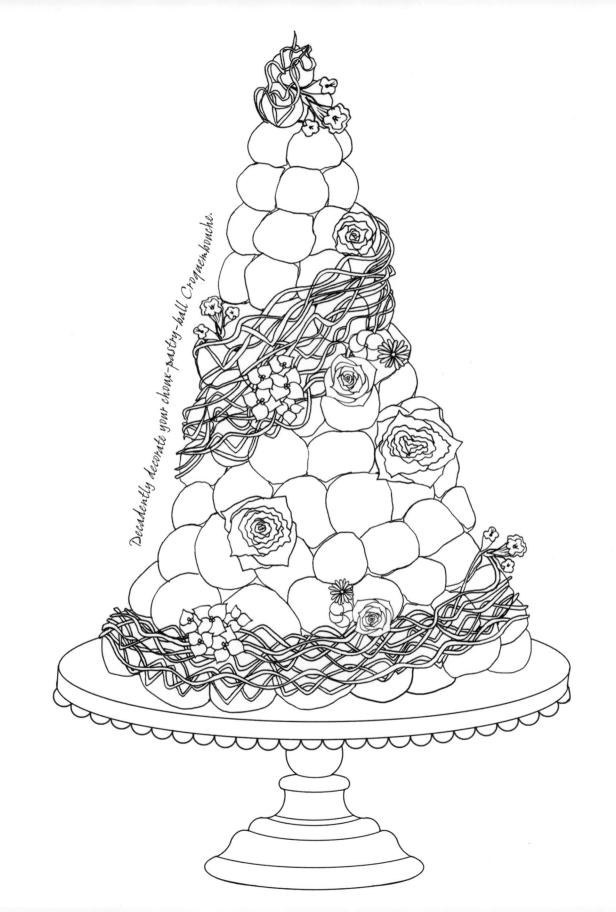

Decadently decorate your choux-pastry-ball Croquembouche.

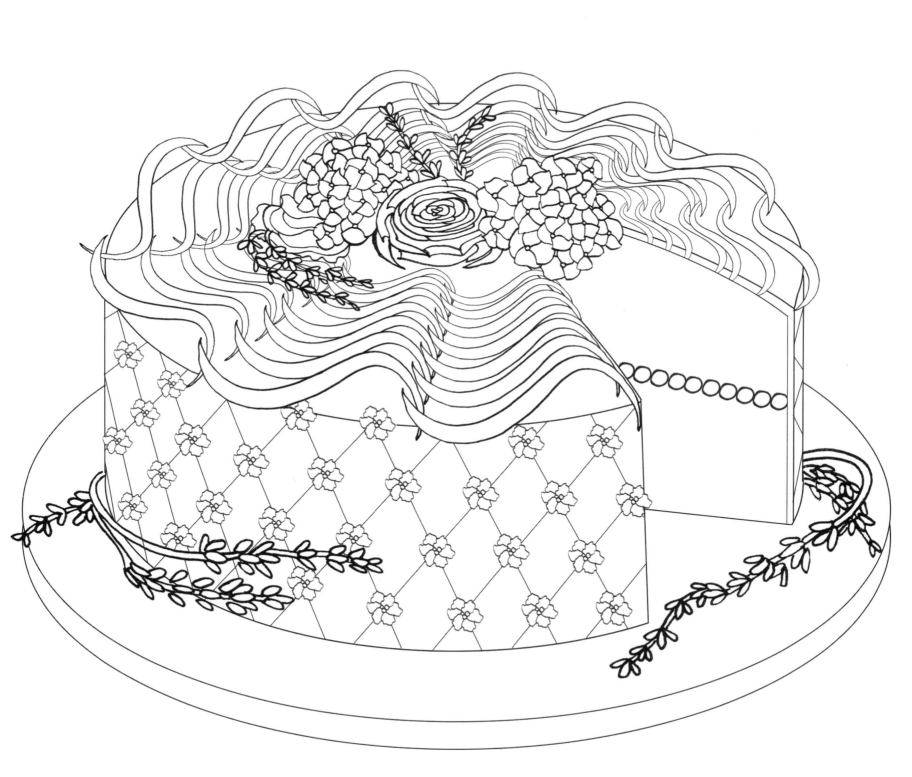

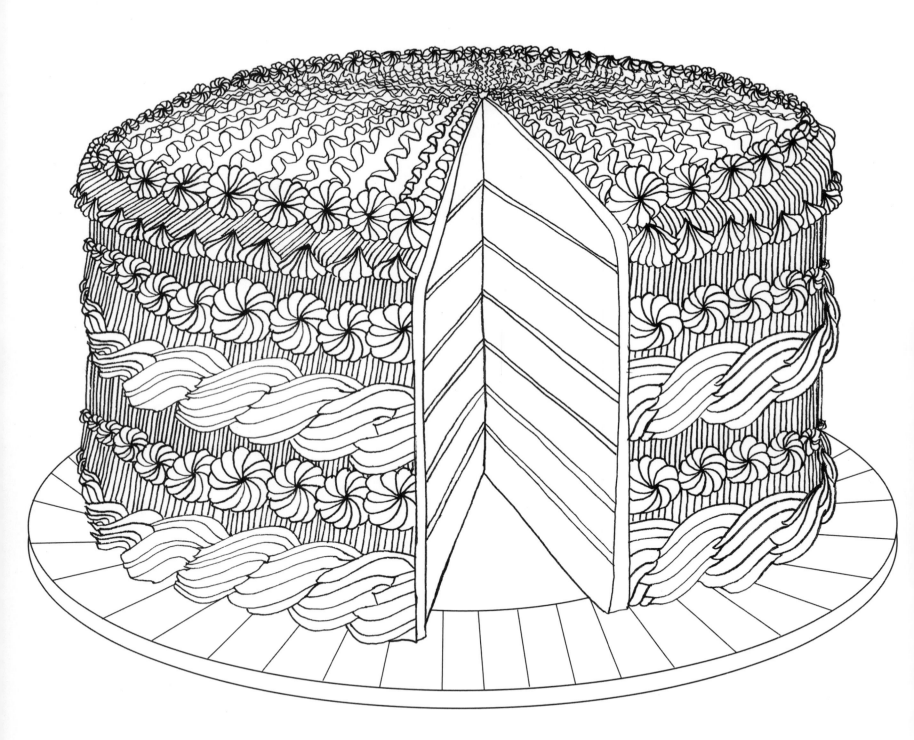

Create your own cakes here . . .

Create your own cakes here . . .